Temptation

Temptation

EROS COMIX™
P.O. Box 25070
Seattle, WA 98125

Edited by **Ezra Mark**
Art Direction by **Victor M.**
Published by **Gary Groth** and **Kim Thompson**
Produced for Eros Comix™ by **Studio Proteus**

ALIMONY HUNTER

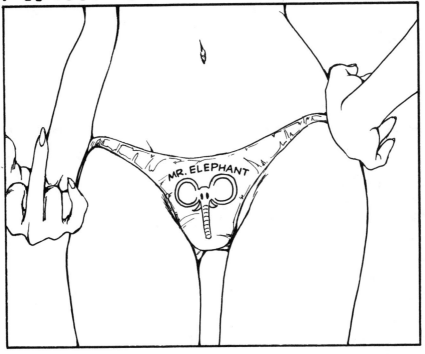

whew...

THAT WAS INCREDIBLE...

AND THEY WERE BOTH WOMEN, TOO!

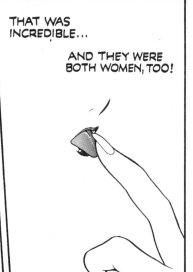

JUST... JUST THINKING ABOUT IT MAKES ME SO HOT...

AHHN!

I'M *JUN NAKATANI*-- THE PLEASURE IS *ALL* MINE.

SO... WHAT'D YOU THINK OF THE SHOW?

GOT YOU WET, DID IT?

I... *Um...*

D-DO YOU ALWAYS DO IT IN PUBLIC?

ARE YOU KIDDING? THE BUS WAS COMING, SO WE JUST HAD TIME FOR A QUICKIE!

BUT THERE'S A REAL THRILL TO IT, THAT'S FOR SURE. I MEAN, YOU COULD GET *CAUGHT!*

I GOTTA ADMIT, THOUGH, I NEVER FIGURED ANYONE WHO CAUGHT US WOULD JUST STAND AND STARE LIKE THAT!

I...UH... I WAS *SHOCKED,* THAT'S ALL!

SO HONEY, HOW FAR ARE YOU GOING?

I...I'M GOING TO SEE MY STEPSON.

THANK YOU FOR CHOOSING THE BORDERLINE EXPRESS. NOW THAT WE'VE REACHED CRUISING SPEED WE'LL BE TURNING OFF THE OVERHEAD LIGHTS...

YOUR STEPSON, HUH...

WHAT?! YOU'RE MARRIED?!

GOD, THAT REALLY SUCKS!

WELL, SORRY TO DISAPPOINT YOU!

I MEAN, YOU'RE SO YOUNG!

AND YOU'RE SO BEAUTIFUL!

MMM...

SLRRPP

TOO TASTY TO WASTE ON ONE MAN!

ARE...
ARE WE
GOING
TO DO IT
HERE?
ON THE
BUS?

JUST
THINK
OF THE
THRILL...

...LITTLE
WIFEY!

AAH,
YESSS!

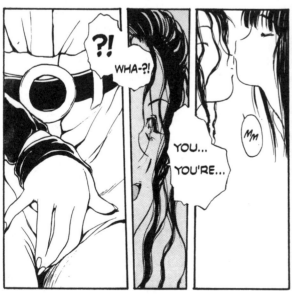

?!

WHA-?!

YOU...
YOU'RE...

MM

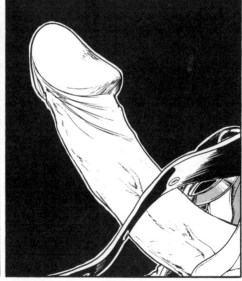

SO LITTLE WIFEY... YOU'VE BEEN PRACTICING!

AW, C'MON!

WHERE ARE YOU STAYING?

I DON'T KNOW YET... AT A FRIEND'S, MAYBE...

WHY DON'T YOU STAY AT MY PLACE? WE CAN TAKE OUR SWEET TIME THERE.

HAHHH...

♬DINGG DONGG♪

HELLO?

KUNIHIKO? IT'S ME, CHIZURU.

CHIZURU?!

GREAT! YOU MADE IT! I'LL BUZZ YOU IN!

SORRY... I SHOULD'VE BEEN AT THE STATION TO SEE YOU!

AW, FORGET IT!

THE MAID SAID YOU'RE REALLY SICK, THIS TIME.

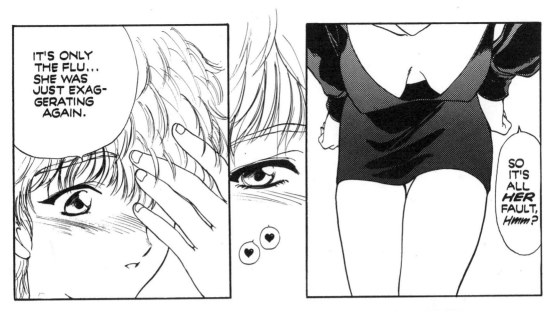

IT'S ONLY THE FLU... SHE WAS JUST EXAGGERATING AGAIN.

SO IT'S ALL *HER* FAULT, *Hmm?*

OH! THIS IS A NEW... UH... *FRIEND* OF MINE.

JUN NAKATANI. JUST CALL ME JUN.

AHEM

NICE TO MEET YOU, MA'AM. I'M KUNIHIKO.

WHAT A CUTIE! I *LIKE* GUYS WITH REAL MANNERS!

HOW'S YOUR FEVER.???

AH?

IT WAS A LONG TRIP, SO WE'RE GONNA FRESHEN UP AND REST IN YOUR DAD'S ROOM, OKAY?

HEY! THAT HURTS! *OW!*

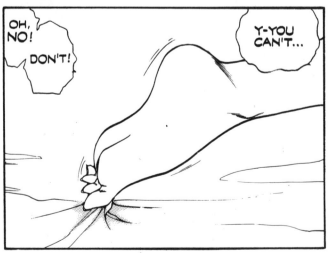

OOH! OH, GOD, CHIZURU, I'M...

I'M GONNA...

SKLSSH

SPLURT!

AHH! ♥

YUMM!

SO MUCH CUM!

YOU WERE SAVING IT UP FOR ME!

YEAH...

HOW SWEET!

GOD, I WANT YOU SO BADLY...

...MY PUSSY'S DRIPPING!

GSSH

THE END

AKIRA

-MIRROR-

YOSHIKO'S IN *LOVE* WITH YOU!

AND YOU'RE... *DOING IT* WITH A *BOY!*

SO? THAT BOY'S IN LOVE WITH ME, TOO.

AND IT DOESN'T MATTER IF IT'S A GIRL OR A BOY.

THEY'RE NOTHING BUT A WARM HOLE FOR MY COME.

OOH! HOW *CAN* YOU!?

AND FUCKING MEN DOESN'T MEAN I CAN'T FUCK WOMEN TOO...DOES IT?

YOU!! YOU ARE A TOTAL *SHIT!*

FWHMP

YOU'RE STRANGE-LY UPSET ABOUT THIS.

YOU HOT FOR ME OR SOME-THING?

WHAT?! YOU GOTTA BE K-KIDDING!

HEY!

FWMP

IF YOU WANT ME TO FUCK YOU, JUST ASK.

I CAN GIVE YOU WHATEVER YOU WANT.

YOU...
YOU ARE **SO**--

I FEEL SORRY FOR YOU.

I'LL BET THERE'S NO ONE YOU'RE IN LOVE WITH!

IS THERE...?

YES, THERE IS.

THERE **IS** ONE PERSON I TRULY LOVE.

BUT...

...I CAN NEVER TELL THAT PERSON HOW I FEEL.

HUNGRY...

SO OTHER PEOPLE ARE JUST MEAT TO ME.

BUT HOW CAN--

AMEMIYA! I'M SORRY-- DID I KEEP YOU WAITING?

SQUEEEK

COLD

!!?

AAGGHN!

NOOOO!
T-TAKE
IT OUT!
TAKE
IT
OUT!

SPLSHH

AH!

AA!

HHNK!

UNhh...

=hahh=

=hahh=

=hahh=

=huhh=

THAT
WAS
SO...
COLD...

KATAK

WOW... STRAIGHT SEX!! WELL, SORT OF...

SHLUUP

OOH... GOD, *NO!* DON'T STOP!

MORE...

P-PLEASE...

~hahh~

AMEMIYA...? WH-WHERE ARE YOU GOING...?

~hahh~

I TOLD YOU *NEVER* TO CALL ME BY MY FIRST NAME.

WHAT?! COME ON-- WHO CARES?!

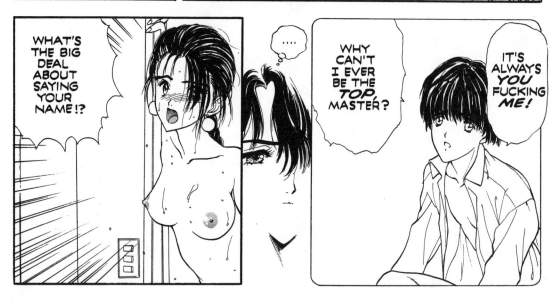

WHAT'S THE BIG DEAL ABOUT SAYING YOUR NAME!?

....

WHY CAN'T I EVER BE THE *TOP,* MASTER?

IT'S ALWAYS *YOU* FUCKING *ME!*

MY NAME AND MY BODY BELONG TO ANOTHER.

I HAVE TO KEEP THOSE PARTS OF ME PURE... UNSULLIED...

WHAT IS *THAT* SUPPOSED TO MEAN?!

GOD, YOU'RE SO *WEIRD!*

HUNGRY...

YOU FUCKING JERK!

YOU SHOULD BE BACK IN THE COUNTRY BY NOW.

PLEASE... CALL ME...

--YA LATER, PAL. BREEP!

BEEEP! HEY, AMEMIYA-- TAMARU HERE. LOOK, I GET PAID NEXT WEEK, SO I'LL HAVE YOUR MONEY BY THEN. SORRY...

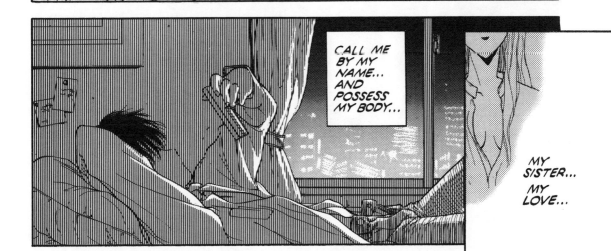

CALL ME BY MY NAME... AND POSSESS MY BODY...

MY SISTER... MY LOVE...

I'LL BE BACK NEXT WEEK. HERE'S YOUR ALLOWANCE FOR THIS MONTH.

THANKS, DEAR.

OK...

SEE YOU LATER.

WHY ARE YOU DOING THIS, YUKA?

SLRPP

MMM...

BECAUSE MY BOY-FRIEND BETRAYED ME.

THAT'S WHY...

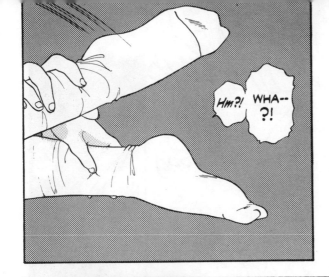

HM?! WHA--?!

...I'M HAVING SEX WITH THE MOST AWFUL MAN I'VE EVER MET.

SHLUUP SHLRRP SLLLP

UHH! UHMM!

AAH!

F-FUCK ME!

SKLSSH

I-- I'M SO FUCKING WET!

-hahh-

-hahh-

YOU WANT IT, SLUT?

TAKE IT!!

SHKK

AAAAH!!

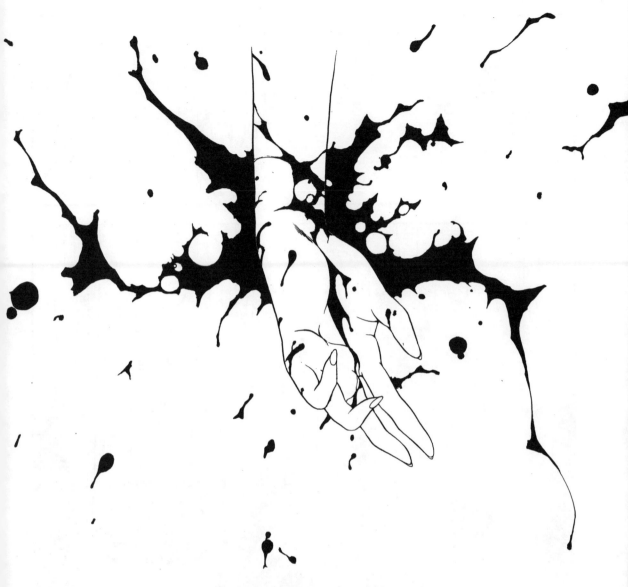

CRIMSON

The Other Tears of a Woman

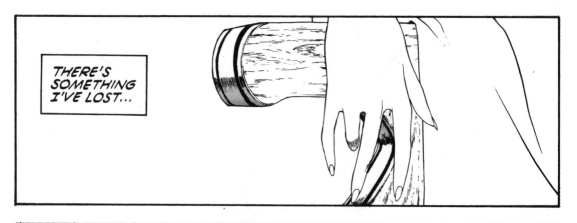

THERE'S SOMETHING I'VE LOST...

I DESIRE IT...
I ACHE FOR IT...

THEIR LOVELINESS CAN DRAW YOU IN...

DID SHE FEEL NO PAIN...? IT SEEMED SO.

SHE SMILED.

SHE WEPT TEARS OF BLOOD, AND YET SHE DID NOT CRY.

BUT THAT EYE!

THAT EYE THAT COULD NOT SEE...

...WAS WATCHING ME!

GOD DAMN IT!!!

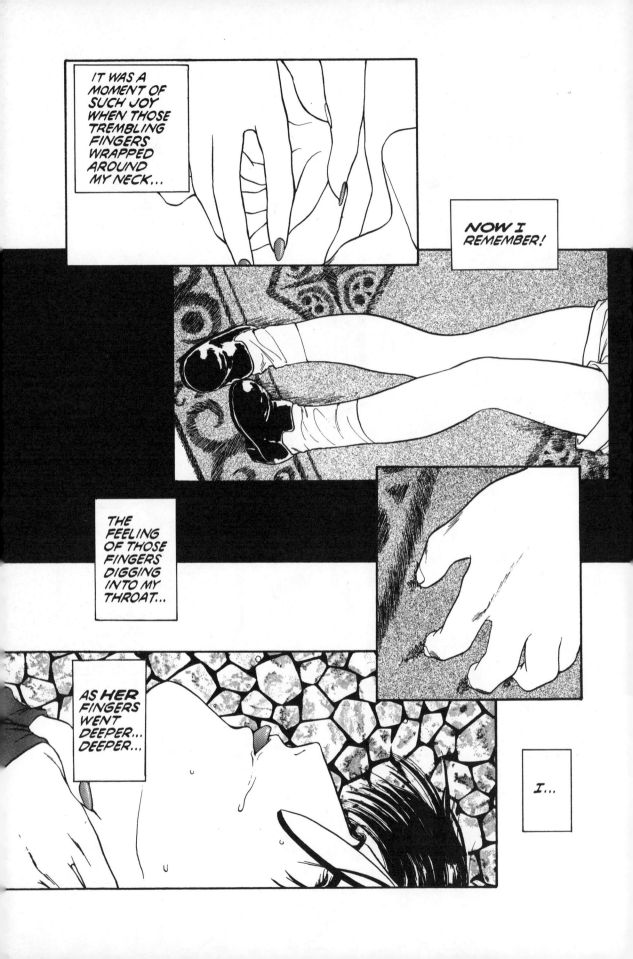

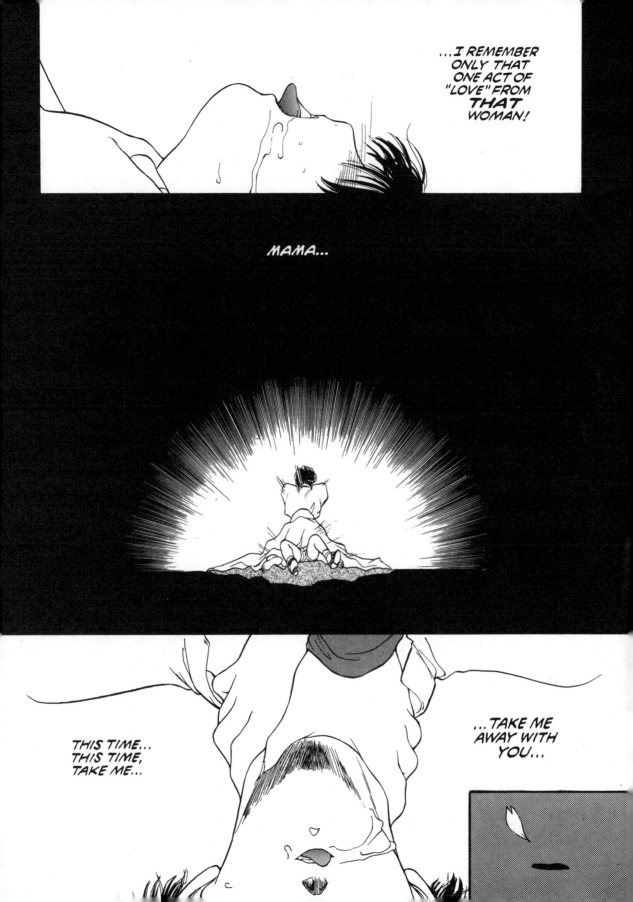

CRIMSON: THE END

Illustration

Gallery

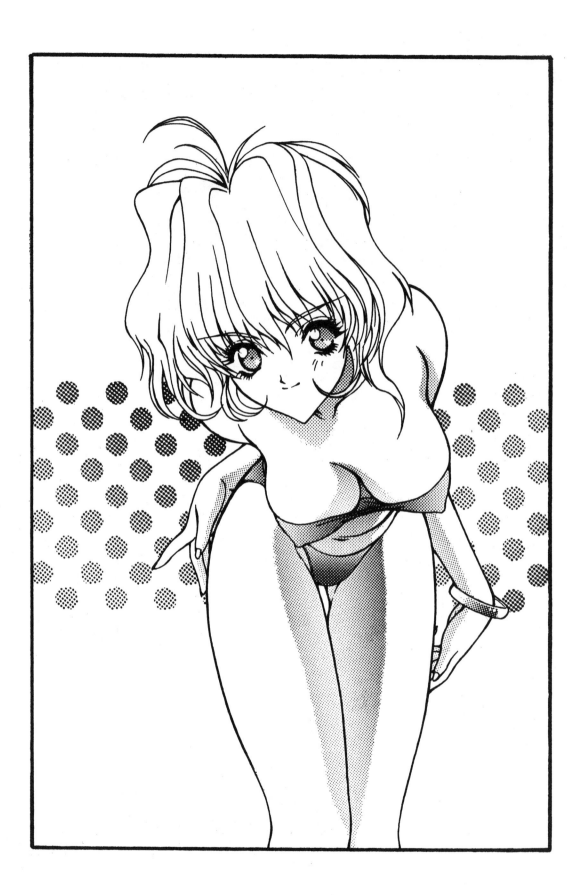